SHOE FULL OF SHAMROCK

SHOE FULL OF SHAMROCK

By Mary Francis Shura

Illustrated by N. M. Bodecker

ATHENEUM 1965 NEW YORK

To
the Sean-Bhean Bhocht
and her scattered riches

CHAPTER I

Davie sat on the bottom step of the front stairs and considered Saturday. The step felt cold under him. The pale February sun buttered the street with light that held no warmth. Small, ragged mounds of snow clustered along the base of the apartment house. In the park across the busy street, a few patches of dark earth showed on the south slopes.

Saturday for grownups was just like every other weekday. They hurried along the street with an air of business as usual. Davie's father had done the same, only turning at the corner to wave one last good-bye before disappearing for the day.

Davie sighed. His father was gone. His friends were gone. He had waved each of them good-bye, acting every time as if he did not care.

Karl, with his hand tight in his Uncle Gus's great red one, had gone off for the day to Brooklyn to play with his cousins. Patrick's grandfather had come early to take him downtown, all the way to Times Square, where they would eat lunch. Even Margot, who was little better than no playmate at all, had gone across the city to spend the day with her older, married sister.

Davie sighed again as he climbed the three flights of stairs to his apartment. He opened the door carefully in case little Megan was already down for her morning nap.

His mother looked up with a smile. "And did you see your father off for the day?" she asked, pushing a loose red curl from her forehead with the back of her hand.

"I did that," Davie told her. "And Karl and Patrick and Margot," he added glumly.

"They're all gone?" She cocked her head to look at him, as she put Megan to bed. The baby's head rolled sleepily when she was laid down. After one humping turn, she drew a tight fist up against her cheek and closed her eyes.

When Davie nodded, his mother made a little clucking noise with her tongue and came over to him.

"Come, now. It's not all that bad, Dave boy. You'll get busy with play and before you know it, dark will be settling in and your father be coming down the street whistling for you."

"It's not like it was only this Saturday, Mom," he told her. "Think how many Saturdays are like this. Everybody has somebody but me. They all have uncles and grandpas to take them places." Davie's voice choked.

"It's sorry I am, and you know it," she told him. "I miss the little jaunts the two of us used to make, before we had Megan. But this is the way of it now."

"It's not that, Mom," Davie replied. "I wouldn't take anything for Megan." He hesitated a minute, uncertain of the quick Irish temper that lay always just behind her gray eyes. "If only Uncle Stephen . . ."

She raised her small hand warningly. "Don't be speaking of Uncle Stephen to me, young man. It's not my fault that he's a hothead." She flushed so that the band of freckles on her nose stood out. Davie bit his lip.

He knew better than to mention Uncle Stephen, but on a day like this he always thought how fine it would be to have his uncle near. They were twins, this Uncle Stephen and his mother, and yet they weren't friends. When Davie had asked his father about it, his father shook his head with a doubtful smile. "That's a pair, those two," he had said. "They've been at hammer and tongs since they were tiny. Alike as two peas they are, yet never able to see eye to eye on the simplest matter."

"Mother won't even let me speak of him," Davie had complained.

"You're a cocky one even to try," his father grinned. "They had their last falling out when your mother and I were wed. When we left Ireland and came to America, they didn't even so much as bid each other good-bye." He added, "I'm fond of Stephen myself, for he's your mother all over again except in size."

"Is he bigger?" Davie had asked. Father had widened his eyes. "Bigger!" he repeated with a loud breath. "He's a giant of a man. He would bend to pass that door, he would. He could pick up the two of us and have strength left over to throw us. He's a giant, that Stephen."

Davie remembered his father reading aloud a letter from the Old Country. It had told of Stephen's leaving Ireland. Davie's mother had been mashing potatoes with a wooden thumper while his father read to her slowly from his perch on the high stool in the kitchen.

She had interrupted, waving the potato thumper in the air. "Just jump over the part about that hothead Stephen," she told Davie's father. "Read it to yourself, if you will, but I've no interest in it." With a toss of her head, she had returned to the potatoes with even greater vigor, as if to thump the picture of Stephen out of her mind.

Davie had thought of the letter often, and he wondered where Uncle Stephen had gone. He tried to remember every word his father had read.

"Times are very poor here," he recalled his grand-mother's words. "There's no work to be had, whether a man's willing or not. There's naught to do but leave Ireland and make a new life. Stephen himself is readying to leave. . . ." It was here that his mother had stopped the reading of the letter.

Many of the men of Ireland came to America. Davie had not dared ask his father where Uncle Stephen had gone. He didn't want to discover that this last hope of an uncle was gone. Davie preferred to think that somewhere in New York, Uncle Stephen strode along like a giant, crowned with a mass of red hair like Davie's own mother's, and that someday Davie would meet him. And they would be friends.

Davie went to the window and stared down into the street. As weak as it was, the sun was melting the snow, and little trickles of dirty water wandered along the street.

It was not until after lunch that his mother had a suggestion.

"I wouldn't be surprised if the ice wasn't melted from the little lake," she said. "You might take a crust of bread to the park and feed the fishes there."

Davie jumped at the idea. The fishes in the park lake were hardly bigger than sewing needles, but they gathered in great clusters to battle for crumbs. Before Megan was born, when Davie had been too little to cross the street alone, his mother and he had fed those fishes almost every afternoon.

While his mother wrapped the bread, Davie put on his jacket and cap. He jumped every other step all the way downstairs.

CHAPTER II

The sidewalks in the park were always full. Old men with canes and young women with children almost filled the paths. Davie cut across the snow-covered grass to reach the lake. He was almost there when he was startled by a sudden bark. A small black dog romped from the bushes and circled him, wagging its tail.

"Hey fellow, hey boy," Davie coaxed, holding out his hand. The pup drew near, then backed away several times before it consented to be petted. It watched Davie's hand warily as he tried to stroke its head. It held still only a minute before bouncing away again as if anxious to play.

"Let me find a stick," Davie called. The dog watched, head cocked, while Davie looked around. Finally, right by the lake, Davie found a branch that had been torn from a tree by winter wind. He laid the package of bread crusts for the fishes carefully under a nearby thorn bush. The brisk wind stirred its wrapper. Davie hesitated and decided to fasten it down. He scraped away the wet leaves under the bush and saw a gray rock set in the soil. Davie tugged at it a moment and was surprised at how quickly it came up. When he lifted it to pin down the wrapped bread, he discovered a small pouch hidden under the rock. Davie

pulled out the pouch and turned it in his hand.

It was a pretty thing, made of rough leather, russet in color, and hand-sewn with smooth leather laces. The drawstring at the neck was tied in an elaborate knot.

The puppy drew near to watch. It barked as if to complain of being deserted.

"Hush, boy," Davie said. The knot was hard to undo, for Davie's fingers became stiff with cold as soon as he took off his mittens. He was still trying to work open the bag when a voice sounded at his elbow.

"And what do you think you're doing with my property?"

Davie jumped with surprise. The small black dog began to bark furiously at the little man who was suddenly standing beside Davie.

The man was no bigger than Davie himself, but man he was, for a wisp of beard circled his chin, and his eyebrows were thick and unruly like tangled twigs along a stream. He was frowning at Davie, his eyes beady bright.

"I say, that's my property," the little man snapped, "and you'd better be giving it to me."

He was leaning so close that Davie took a firmer hold on the pouch, not at all sure that the man wouldn't try to grab it from his hand.

"How am I to be knowing it's yours?" Davie asked,

feeling the pouch as he spoke. It felt, through the rough leather, as if it held coins. In his heart he didn't doubt that it really was the little man's own pouch, for he had come so swiftly. But Davie was curious, and after all it had been there under the thorn bush, not in any proper place at all.

"It's only because you're a good Irishman that I offer this," the little man said, eyeing Davie. "But because you are, and because I'm so fair, I'll make a deal with you."

Davie said nothing, for the little man seemed to forget that Davie was the one with the pouch.

"If you give me my property," the little man coaxed, "I'll make you a solemn promise that you'll never have rheumatism again as long as you live."

Davie grinned. "That's no bargain; I've never had it."

The little man's face fell, and he studied Davie thoughtfully. "Then there's a spell I can say . . ." He leaped up, waving his hands dramatically. "Just for the return of my pouch, you will be given a voice as pure as a robin's, as sweet as a plum cake, and as strong as a thorn club!"

Davie's eyes widened with horror. "No thanks!" he said. "And me have to spend two afternoons a week singing with the choir? And be forever standing for company and showing off when I'd rather be sitting by the others giggling and laughing?"

The little man sat down cross-legged on the ground,

18

looking very dejected. He frowned and mumbled and glared at Davie. Davie stroked the black dog, which leaned against him and looked at him lovingly while they waited.

"Then what in the world do you want?" the little man asked finally.

It was like those stories Davie's father had told him in which there came a minute when the hero had a wish or three that he could make. Davie had thought it over a lot and had planned to be ready when such a time came.

But here it was, and he wasn't ready at all.

19

The things that story people always asked for would not be useful to him—David Meehawl O'Sullivan, on the west side of New York on a cold Saturday. What would he do with a princess? Or a great pile of money which would surely just be spent, as his father's paycheck was, for milk and potatoes and shoes for school?

Davie was still staring at the man and thinking when he heard the familiar long, shrill whistle. He looked up with astonishment to find that the sky was dusky with evening.

Davie stuffed the pouch into his jacket pocket and set off running toward his father, who was whistling across the park for him.

When Davie looked back, the little man was gone. The black puppy had pulled the parcel of bread from under the stone and was gnawing it. The pouch felt heavy and unfamiliar in Davie's pocket, and the weight of it there made his heart thump.

Thinking it over later, it seemed like something Davie had imagined. The only way that he could reassure himself that he had met the strange small man was by getting out the little pouch and looking at it. He couldn't really explain to himself why he had told no one about it. After he and Father got home, Davie hid the pouch in his closet with his private things. It was not until later, when everyone thought he was asleep, that he took it out and examined it.

The pouch held seventeen gold coins. They looked very old and had strange letters on them that Davie could not read. He sat a long time turning them in his hands, wondering about them. If the pouch belonged to the little man, why had he hidden it under the thorn bush instead of carrying it about with him? And why had the little man disappeared when Davie's father came into the park?

CHAPTER III

The snow returned that week with as much vigor as if winter had not been to New York at all that year. Great piles of snow gathered along the streets, and the wind blew so bitterly that Davie was not tempted to play outside at all, much less go into the park.

After supper on those cold, wintry evenings, Megan would drowse in her nightdress on Mother's lap or sit and play with kitchen spoons, while Mother's quick hands worked her knitting. After he had read the paper, Davie's father would pull lazily on his pipe and tell wonderful tales to Davie of the way life had been in the Old Country when he was a boy and Davie's mother was one of the little red-headed O'Flaherty twins.

"Coming home from the fair at Dublin," he told Davie one night, "it grew late, and Seumas, my friend, and I were loathe to cross the bog for fear of the little people.

"We came to a farmer's house and asked him if we could stay the night in his warm barn."

Davie interrupted. "Excuse me, Father," he asked, "but why were you afraid?"

Davie's father laughed, "It was different there in Ireland, Son. There were many wee people whose time for

mischief was after the night fell. We were two young and foolish boys and not given over to courage."

"Tell me about the little people," Davie urged. From the corner of his eye, Davie could see his mother's frown of disapproval, but his father talked on.

"Well, there are the banshees who howl at night when there is a death in the house, and they are fearsome to hear. There are the people of Shee . . . that is, the fairyfolk. They are forever stirring up all the mischief they can find. And the leprecauns . . . always we kept a sharp watch for them, thinking that this way a fortune could be made."

"How is that?" Davie asked.

His father raised his hands in pretended horror, then puffed on his pipe, shaking his head dolefully.

"For a great boy who's almost eight, you know nearly nothing," he said. "There's a pot of gold that belongs to every leprecaun family," he explained. "They clip it, a shred at a time, off the money of big people. If you should catch a leprecaun, he gives this gold to you for ransom."

"Can't you just take it from him?"

"Aye, but there's never a little man that would carry gold with him. It's safely hidden under a thorn bush, it is! And you'd never be finding it except by happy chance. Thorn bushes, like robins, are special. Anything beneath a thorn bush is under the protection of fairies."

"What would a leprecaun do in New York, Father?" Davie asked thoughtfully.

"A leprecaun in New York, indeed," his mother snorted. "Look at the ideas you're putting in that boy's head. First we know, he'll be seizing up a little man somewhere, and we'll be explaining it to the patrolman."

"Ah, Caitilin, it's no matter. The boy knows better." But Davie's father grew thoughtful. "It would be a hard life for him indeed, Davie boy. In the Old Country, there's always a bit of bread and milk or stirabout that is put where the little people can find it. A leprecaun would be like to starve in this land with the wind so chill and him so little."

"But they would have their gold," Davie said.

"Aye, they would need it, come so cold a time."

Davie never did hear the end of his father's story of Seumas and the warm barn. His mother rose briskly with Megan sound asleep in her arms.

"Off to bed, young David," she said sternly. "You're better to be sleeping against tomorrow's school day than to be talking of little folk in this far place. A leprecaun in New York, indeed!"

A fresh snow came that night. It didn't fall. It was whipped down the street so that it clung in freezing puffs to the rough red bricks. The wind howled into Davie's dream like a banshee, and he woke with a fearful start.

Davie went to the window with a blanket pulled about him and looked out. He could not even see the street through the driving flakes. He thought of the park with its cold gray stones and its trees bending in the wind, and of the little man so small with only that jacket on.

"A leprecaun in New York, indeed!" Mother had said. Davie could not go back to sleep until he had buried his head under the covers to shut away the sound of the wind and the wet slip-slosh of the snow driven across the window pane.

The next morning, Davie left earlier than usual for school. He told Patrick and Karl not to wait for him. Even with his boots on, it was hard to make his way across the deep drifts to the edge of the lake. At last he found the thorn bush. A few frozen berries still clung to its icy branches. He dug way down to the earth. His eyes stung from cold, and he might as well have had no mittens at all for the good they did, all sodden from the snow. The rock still had the little crevice under it. Davie fitted the pouch back into its hole. When he was finished, he piled up the snow again so that no chance passerby would notice what had been done.

His eyes were streaming and his nose was an aching blue. But even with the little steamy soreness coming on his legs where his wet trousers rubbed, he felt better all that day.

CHAPTER IV

Davie did not see the little man again for several weeks. But there were a great many times he thought about him and the gold he had put back under the thorn bush. Once between snows, Davie looked under the bush and found the pouch was gone. There was only that hollow place under the rock filled with frozen water.

Davie's shoes grew very thin. His mother frowned when she looked at them. "Maybe soon we can get you new ones," she told him.

Megan had her first birthday at the end of February. She took three wide-legged, staggering steps that same day. They all laughed and clapped with pride so that she fell, frightened, and sat crying with anger at the lot of them. Davie was allowed to eat all the currants from Megan's piece of cake, for she had too few teeth to chew them.

Although Davie had made a book of colored pictures for her birthday gift, he kept thinking of what he could have given her if he had kept the pouch of gold.

March came like a burst of teasing laughter. It swept the snow from the streets and found last year's rubbish beneath it. Everything blew . . . the clouds, the newspapers from the corner stand, and Davie's hat.

Davie was running his kite across the park. He pulled his hat low over his ears, and still the wind caught it and rolled it wildly across the grass into a thicket.

Davie crouched on the wet grass and peered into the dark of the thicket. The hat was gone. He stared hard. The wind could not move in such a place, and Davie had seen the hat blow in there.

At last he rose and shrugged. He was brushing off his soiled knees when he heard the little man's laughter.

"And what would you be trading for an old dirty hat that I found in the thicket on a windy March day?"

Davie looked all about before he spied the little old man sitting cross-legged above him on the branch of a big tree. Davie laughed in spite of himself, for the little man was wearing Davie's schoolboy hat set at a jaunty angle on top of his own pointed cap.

"I'll tell you what I'll do," Davie laughed. "If you give me my property, I'll make a spell that you won't have rheumatism again as long as you live."

The little man scowled fiercely and jumped down from the tree. He landed close to Davie and frowned up at him.

"It's not fit that a good Irish lad should be making light of spells," he rebuked Davie.

"Is it fit that a man should be getting his gold back and never saying a thank you for it?" Davie countered.

The little man ducked his head and did not look at Davie at all.

"It's a new thing, that's what it is," the little man complained. "There's always been a bit of an enmity between your people and mine. A fellow doesn't rightfully know what to say when his enemy acts like a friend." He twisted his mouth as if it hurt. "But thank you, that's what. Thank and bless you, and may all your mornings come in the full sun."

"But, mind you, I was asking for no favors," he added. "I was willing to make a trade, I was."

"That's all right," Davie said, trying to hide his laughter at the little fellow's embarrassment. "But I need to have my cap back."

The little man pulled it off and studied it before handing it to Davie.

Davie almost had it in his hand when the little man grabbed it back again. Turning away from Davie, he crouched over the hat and worked busily with his hands, doing something with it that Davie could not see, no matter how hard he strained to look.

When the little man turned about again, he was smiling.

"What were you doing to my hat?" Davie demanded.

"Nothing much," the little man said, grinning now. "Wear it in peace!" He stuck both hands in the pockets

CHAPTER V

Davie put the little plant to grow in a blue bowl that was too big for Megan's serving of porridge and too small for his own. There was just room for it to stand on his windowsill. His mother smiled as he went from the kitchen each morning with a little glass of water for it.

"And how does your garden grow, Davie boy?" she would ask, turning from her work to watch him. "It's curious I am to see what kind of a plant you've brought home to care for."

Davie was curious, too, but it soon became only a part of his day's habit to water it, for there were other things on his mind. It would seem that the shining sun of March would bring more laughter into the small rooms of their apartment, but it did not.

Davie's father, who used to bound whistling up the stairs and open the door with a gay shout, came slowly now. Listening to his heavy footsteps on the stairs made a sadness in Davie, like listening to late bells from a far church.

Oh, his father smiled and was merry once he was home. He would lift Megan high, swinging her fat little body over his head to make her giggle. She clutched at his dark

hair so fiercely that Father had to twist his head this way and that to escape her fingers.

But Davie noticed that when his father was not talking to him or playing with Megan, he looked different. A shadow of unhappiness lay across his face like a cloud darkening a sunny day.

His mother, too, was different. Sometimes when Davie came home from school, he was almost sure that her eyes were too bright, as if she had just been crying.

Once, when he asked her, she made a great to-do about it. "Crying indeed! And why should I be crying with such a fine lad as you and baby Megan for company and every night himself coming home? It's a head for stories you have, and you better be about your studies or you'll have to be making them up for the teacher in the way of an excuse." .

It was not many days later that Davie realized the change in his mother and father had something to do with the letters which were coming from Ireland more often now.

One lonely Saturday, when all his playmates were off with their uncles or grandfathers, the mailman came while Davie was sitting on the steps. Davie studied the letter as he carried it upstairs. The handwriting, which he had been told was his grandfather's, trailed like the webbing of spiders across the thin envelope. Davie could barely make out the name of the sender.

Davie's mother dropped her work and sat on her kitchen stool to tear open the envelope with trembling fingers. When she looked up and saw Davie watching, she waved him away.

"Run, Davie lad," she said, "and leave me in peace. Go and water that little garden you have, but mind you don't wake Megan going past her bed."

From his window, Davie saw a sudden movement outside. He watched carefully a moment before running to the closet for his cap. Holding the feather in his hand, he looked at the bird that was searching for worms in the park across the street. Sure enough, it was a robin—the same brown and red as the feather the little man had given him.

A cart clattered down the street, startling the bird. It rose in flight and disappeared into the park.

"When I have watered my plant, I shall feed that bird," Davie promised himself. He sloshed the water quickly on his little plant, and then his eyes widened.

"Mother," he cried, "Mother, Mother, come and see!" In his excitement, he forgot her wish to be left alone. He went running into the kitchen but stopped in dismay. She was still sitting with her head bent over. The letter was crumpled in her hands, and her shoulders shook with sobs.

Davie burst into tears himself for no reason he knew except that he loved her, and this made her grief his own. He ran to her and put his arms around her.

"Don't cry, Mother, please don't cry," he begged. He cried harder himself as he said the words.

He could feel her draw a strong breath that tightened her dress against him. Her hands patted him gently. "Davie, Davie," she said, sniffling a little. She wiped her eyes on the top of her apron. "We'll both stop, we will . . . great babies we are, worse than Megan herself."

After a minute she spoke again with a brightness that he knew she had to put there, for it sprang from no happiness inside her.

"Why did you call me? What did you want, Son?"

Davie sniffed hard, trying to be as strong as she. "It's my plant, Mother," he said. "All the round green things have come of a sudden to leaves, and it's strange."

"I'll come and see!" She folded the letter carefully into her pocket and went with him, her arm about his shoulders.

When Mother stood in the doorway, she seemed to forget that Megan was curled in sleep in the other bed. She clapped her hands in amazement, and her happiness sounded real this time.

"Would you look at that?" she cried. "It is . . . it truly is! The blessed plant itself, and it growing like a weed on this boy's window . . . and in this far place." For a moment it sounded as if she might cry again.

"But what is it?" Davie asked, "I've never seen such a plant before."

His mother knelt by the window, and the sun coming in brightened the freckles on her nose.

"It's a shamrock, that's what it is," she declared, touching the tips of the newly uncurled leaves with a careful finger. "And it's the first that I've seen since your father and I came to this country."

"Wherever did you get this blessed plant?" she asked. "It must be a sign." She shook her head and wiped the corner of one eye.

"Shamrock . . ." Davie repeated slowly.

Davie's mother sat by the window, drawing her knees up under her chin and holding the little bowl tenderly.

"Look at it, Son," she said. "For there's more than the green of growing in *this* plant.

"You remember that Saint Patrick himself was once only a Roman boy, the heir to a senator named Calpernius, who was stationed in Wales. They lived grandly for those times. But King Naill of our own Ireland, who was but a pagan, sent forth raiders into Wales. Among others, they stole away the boy Patrick, who was about fifteen. They made him a shepherd, and he watched the sheep and the

swine for his masters on the hill called Slemish, which is between Antrim and Down.

"His prayers on this wild hill were finally answered, and he escaped, sailing with a cargo of great wolfhounds through Southern Gaul and finally back to Rome. Not until he was an old man did his fine dream of bringing a mission to Ireland become fulfilled. On that same hill where he had watched his sheep, he held church in a wee barn, the first Christian church in the whole of Ireland it was.

"And, Davie my boy, all the while that Saint Patrick was driving evil from Ireland, his shoes were stained with the green of the shamrock. For you see, this plant grows in the shape of a cross, and shamrock leaves have a peculiar dark shadow which makes them unlike the clover that grows in any other land. And the green of Ireland is the shamrock clothing its hills, and the sweet scent of the shamrock is the perfume of that air."

She sat silent a moment with Davie. Into their silence came the sound of Davie's father on the stairs. His mother began to cry again. Awkwardly, because she could not see through her tears, she pulled the letter from her pocket and shoved it into Davie's hand.

"Give this to your father, lad," she said. "I cannot face doing it for myself."

Davie's father took a long time to read the letter, forming the words silently with his lips. When he had finished, he bowed his head a minute, and then pulled Davie between his knees.

"It's bad news, isn't it, Father?" Davie asked.

"Bad for us, Davie lad, and for your mother's poor old father. It tells that her mother, who has been very ill and in great pain, will suffer no more."

Davie's father answered his questioning look with only a nod. Davie wept against his father's shoulder for the grandmother he had never known.

"Aye, if there was one wish I could claim," Davie's father said, "it would be money enough to bring that lonely man to this place where you and Megan and his own Caitilin would brighten his last days."

"Does it take very much money to bring a grandfather from Ireland, Father?" Davie asked, thinking again of the seventeen pieces of gold.

"More than you or I see in a year, Davie lad," he sighed. "Up now," he set Davie gently aside. "I must go to your mother."

CHAPTER VI

Now that he had a wish to make, a real one, Davie grew fearful. Each day he kept back half of his breakfast and carried it to the park for the robins. There were more now. Sometimes three or four would peer from the small tree at the edge of the park as he scattered breadcrumbs for them.

But the wish. How should he phrase it? How would he know that the little man could really make this wish come true? Sure, the shamrock grew steadily in his window, and every day he took one small leaf of it and wore it inside his shoe so he would always have his luck about him.

But how would it ever be, even with the spring buds bursting on the park trees, how would the streets of New York ever look green like the hills of the Old Country?

Davie's mother did not cry again when Davie was watching. Often he saw her standing by the window of his room, touching the shamrock plant with her fingertips, while her eyes seemed to look out the window and past the park to some far place that he could not see.

One Thursday morning, Davie was making a game of his porridge. With his spoon he piled up a hill in the center of the bowl so that the milk ran all around it like a river. He was about to make a tunnel through it when his father looked over at him and announced, "Davie . . . I just thought of something! Do you know what day it is?"

"Thursday," Davie answered, so surprised by the excitement in his father's voice that he let his spoon fall right on the mountain.

"Thursday, indeed," his father laughed. "It's more than that, it is. It's the seventeenth." He waited, as if this should mean something to Davie. Davie groped in his mind, but the seventeenth still meant nothing.

"March the seventeenth!" his father leaned across the table, his eyes twinkling. "It's the day of St. Patrick, lad, and every Irishman in New York . . . aye, and in all of America, will be wearing a little green on him today because of the Saint himself."

Davie jumped up. "Would you like some of my shamrock to be wearing on your coat, Father?" he offered.

"That I would," his father replied. "It's a good lad that grows his own luck in a porridge bowl."

The sprig of shamrock did look fine against his father's dark coat, Davie thought as he watched him leave. His mother rose on tiptoe to kiss his father's cheek and gave him his hat, after one final rub and a brushing of it with her hand.

Father winked back at Davie and made a quick clucking sound.

"It's a great day for the Irish, lad," he told Davie from the door, "and the very streets will look green!"

Davie sat a moment frozen with amazement. The very streets look green?

"What did Father mean, Mother?" he asked. "What streets will look green? Our streets? New York's streets?" He was bouncing with excitement, and his mother gently pushed him back into his chair.

"Finish your porridge. It's a bit of nonsense, but good nonsense, I suppose."

"Tell me about it," Davie insisted.

"Eat, or I won't," his mother said. She sat across from him with her arms folded. "Eat now," she repeated.

Davie swallowed reluctant bites as he listened.

"There's a great lot of us, you know, we Irish in America. On St. Patrick's day, even those other people who talk light of the Irish like to join the fun. They say, though I've never seen it myself, that downtown the big streets are crowded with people wearing green, and all the Irishmen who can take the day from their work make a grand parade."

"Parade?" Davie asked, his eyes wide.

She nodded her head, smiling in spite of herself. "Now eat."

Davie filled his spoon again, even though the last bite lay like a sleepy bird just under his collar.

Davie awkwardly fished for his pennies as the policeman settled him in the saddle. "I'd be happy to pay you," Davie offered.

The officer clucked at his horse and grinned. "You'd better be hanging onto those pennies, lad, for you'll be hungry and cold when the parade is over. See that?"

Davie looked up. A dark mass of clouds was moving over the sun.

"There'll be rain before lunch, mind my words."

The crowd grew thicker as Davie and the policeman went farther downtown. Then Davie saw the parade assembling. All around them was a great din of musical instruments being tuned and men shouting to each other as horses reared on the crowded street.

"You know who you are to meet?" the policeman asked, as he swung Davie down.

Davie nodded, confused by all the noise. He seemed to be surrounded by miles of tall buildings with a forest of flags growing between them.

"Thank you," Davie shouted after the policeman, who waved back and wheeled his horse to join the other mounted police.

Davie pressed himself back against a building and watched the parade begin. There were other children. They were running in every direction, all wearing paper shamrocks or strange little round green hats. Many of the ladies who swept by wore small clay pipes, such as his father smoked, pinned against paper shamrocks on their coats.

And sure enough, everyone was wearing green, like the shamrock that had grown in Davie's window and which now made a painful lump inside his right shoe.

Davie watched the people go by. There was not a soul among them that he knew. He listened to the skirl of the bagpipes and the gay jig tunes that the bands played. He had heard his father and mother sing many of those tunes.

He began to walk along, following the parade. What had the little man said? That he should feed the first robin of the spring, that he should wear a bit of shamrock for luck, and on the day that the streets looked green, his secret wish would come true.

"I wish for enough money for Grandfather to come to America," he said almost aloud. He kept repeating his wish as he jogged along, not knowing what to look for, or what to do to make the wish come true.

Block after block, the parade went on. The threatening clouds began to drop a spattering of rain, and umbrellas blossomed among the crowds lining the street. From above him, Davie could hear the slam of windows being shut against the storm.

The lump of shamrock in Davie's shoe seemed to grow, so that every step he took hurt more. But still he ran on, repeating his wish lest the moment arrive and he miss having it right on the tip of his tongue. The rain grew heavier, blurring Davie's view of the street ahead. Davie ran and ran, sometimes on the sidewalk and sometimes in the street, unable to keep a straight course with the pushing crowds and the slippery pavement.

Then, he thought he saw the little man. Way back in the parade was a cart all trimmed with green paper that was stained and shriveling from the rain. Davie was almost sure he saw the little man himself up on the cart, with his pointed hat and the wisp of his beard damp about his face. Davie tried to run faster and to cross the street to where the cart would pass.

Suddenly he slipped. Davie heard a cry of warning just as he fell, and his head cracked sharply against the curbstone. He heard jumbled thunder of horses' hooves very near and glimpsed the shining metal on uniforms above the polished boots of the marchers.

Then there was nothing.

CHAPTER VII

Davie opened his eyes slowly. Then he shut them tightly again.

"There's a lad," a man's voice boomed at him. "Easy now, try to sit up. How are you, anyway?"

Davie looked at the man and sat bolt upright. The minute he did, he felt as if a hammer were hitting against his head. He moaned.

"Are you all right now?" the voice came again. The pain in Davie's head seemed to come between himself and the voice, making the words sound strange and distant.

"I'm all right, I think," Davie replied.

"What's your name, boy?" the man asked. "Who are you with?"

Davie shook his head. "O'Sullivan, sir," he mumbled. "Davie O'Sullivan, and I came by myself."

He heard the booming voice repeat his name. When he looked again, Davie saw a huge policeman pushing his way through the crowd that had gathered about him. The people stepped back to let the big man through. The rain dripped from the rim of his cap as he leaned over.

"Davie O'Sullivan, is it?" The policeman's face was stern. "Let's have a look at you."

He helped Davie to his feet. Even standing, Davie's chin came only to the level of the man's belt. Davie tried to stand very tall, but his foot hurt too badly for that. He shifted his weight uncomfortably while the big man leaned back to watch him.

"Are you lame?" he asked.

"No, sir," Davie replied.

"Then put your foot down," the policeman commanded, looking at Davie as if he were trying to think something out.

Davie took off his shoe and pulled out the bunch of shamrock so that he could stand. The big man frowned and took the shamrock in his hand, studying it.

After a moment, he turned to another policeman who had come to disperse the crowd. "I'll take care of this one," he said. "After he's safe at home, I'll report in."

Davie felt like a child, like Megan even, being carried into a little restaurant, where he was rubbed dry with a towel before the policeman set him down on a chair.

"Bring a mug of hot milk and a sweet bun," he told the waitress. "This one is chilled to the bone."

The restaurant was brightly lit against the gloom of the rain still falling outside. Davie cupped his chilled fingers around the hot mug. The policeman set his hat on the chair between them and measured sugar into his tea. Davie

watched him silently. He had never seen such a big man, and with such thick red hair.

"Now how is it that you came to be running in front of horses with no proper coat on and a shoe full of shamrock making you lame?" The policeman looked straight at Davie as he spoke, and Davie felt a quick hard thump inside his chest. The man's eyes were gray, and there was all that red hair . . .

"You look like my Uncle Stephen," Davie blurted.

The gray eyes facing Davie widened with surprise. "What kind of an answer is that?"

"It's just that you look like what my father says that my Uncle Stephen is like, sir," he said.

"And how is that?"

"Like my mother, but big as a giant."

"And her name?" the policeman leaned forward a little, his eyes intent on Davie.

"Caitilin O'Flaherty, before she was an O'Sullivan."

A small, almost sweet, smile began to tease the man's mouth. "No bigger than my hand, this world is shrinking," he said. "So you're Caity's boy, and you've the green eyes of the O'Sullivans, haven't you?"

"I suppose so." Davie held his breath, then asked. "Are you my Uncle Stephen, sir?"

The big man's smile became a grin. He ruffled Davie's wet hair. "I am that, David O'Sullivan," he said. "And proud to claim such a one as you."

CHAPTER VIII

Uncle Stephen took Davie home in a horse cab. Try as he would to hold them back, Davie exploded with one sneeze after another.

"Listen to you," Uncle Stephen muttered. "That's what comes of parading around in the rain. What kind of a mother is that Caity anyway, letting a young lad like you run about the streets, falling under horses and catching your death of cold, when you ought to be in school?"

His sudden anger would have frightened Davie except that it was so like his mother's. "She thinks I'm at school," Davie admitted. "And she's the best mother ever. I came on the sly, because I was told that on such a day I could get my wish."

"Wish, shamrock, you're a real Irishman, Davie O'Sullivan, and as silly-headed as your own mother, be she my sister or no. Now, tell me, what wish was worth knocking your head and laming your foot?"

Davie hung his head. It did seem silly-headed for him to have believed that in this parade such a wish would come true.

"Out with it, Davie," Uncle Stephen urged. "What were you wishing for, lad?"

"I was wishing for a way to bring my grandfather from Ireland to our own home . . . now that he's alone." Davie added the last quietly.

Uncle Stephen said nothing. He stared straight ahead as the cab turned the last corner and pulled to a stop at the curb.

Uncle Stephen insisted that he himself would knock on the door, and he would not let Davie down from his arms while he did it. "You'll not be standing on that blistered foot for a while if you're smart," he told Davie.

At her cry of alarm, Davie spoke quickly to his mother. "I'm all right, really I am, Mother. Uncle Stephen . . ."

"Stephen!" she cried, only then recognizing the man who was holding Davie in the dark of the hall. "Come in, both of you! Whatever in this world?"

Once inside, the light of the room seemed filled with the red glow of Uncle Stephen's and Mother's hair as they faced each other over Davie. Davie watched them look at each other. He saw their slow smiles start. Suddenly, he found himself shaken with the laughter that exploded from Uncle Stephen like a spout of steam from a bubbling kettle.

Setting Davie down on a chair, he picked up Davie's mother and swung her about as Father did little Megan.

"If you're not a sight for tired eyes, Caitilin," he laughed. "Rosy as a radish and twice as pretty. Aye, what's

this?" Putting down Davie's mother, he threw up his hands as if in horror, as Megan toddled to the doorway and peeked in at them. "A little beauty it is . . . and the picture of her mother!"

Davie's mother was all flustered. "Let me make tea. Sit down. Have off your coat. Such a fine coat it is." She turned it, admiring the buttons. "A policeman you are!" She kept spinning one way and another, getting nothing done, while Uncle Stephen lured Megan into the crook of his arm, where she finally sat, smiling and lunging for handfuls of his red hair.

Davie's mother finally went off to the kitchen to set a pot to boil. Almost immediately, she reappeared in the doorway and stood with her arms crossed, glaring at Davie. "And you've some explaining to do, young man. Why aren't you in school?" She pressed both hands to her head and shook it back and forth distractedly. "I don't know what this day has come to."

"Just brew the tea," Uncle Stephen laughed. "I'll tend to this one." He did, too. He made Davie get out of his wet clothes and go straight to bed with a patch on his head and one on his foot. Davie slept and wakened again and again to the sound of their talk and laughter in the next room.

It was Davie's father who ended the day as he had begun it, with joy. He came quietly into the room where

Davie lay in the twilight stifling his sneezes in a big hand-kerchief.

He took Davie's hand in his. Davie could barely see his smile in the dim light that came through the window past the naked little stumps of the shamrock plant.

"I don't suppose I'll ever be understanding all of this day, Davie," he said, "but would you listen to them in there . . . the two of them, as happy as potatoes in a pot? They are plotting, they are. Your Uncle Stephen has plenty of money for the trip from Ireland but no home fit for your grandpa. He'll be sending for the old fellow to come, and your grandpa will make his home with your mother and you and Megan and me."

Davie sat up in bed. "Then Grandpa will really come and live with us always here in America?" he asked, want-ing to hear the words said over and over again, for it was such a grand wish to have come true.

"Aye, that is how it will be."

"Father," Davie said, after a while, "I thought Mother and Uncle Stephen didn't like each other at all, but there they are . . . like you say, happy as two potatoes in a pot. What made them change?"

Davie's father smiled. "The same thing, Davie, that turns winter to spring, and a little plant into a shamrock. They'll be saying now that you're as bull-headed as

Stephen, and Megan as silly-headed as Caity, and that they had to make peace to protect themselves against you. Pay them no mind."

Davie's father was at the door when he called back, "And Davie, your Uncle Stephen says that you must quit that sneezing and get well now. It seems that he likes to go jaunting about on Saturdays and needs a boy to take along. Do you think you could manage the time?"

"Could I?" Davie squealed, with a sneeze coming right in the middle. "Could I ever!"

He was just drifting to sleep again when he remembered that his school books had been under that thorn bush in the rain all day long. He groaned and turned over.

Tomorrow he would have to go for them, first thing.

Tomorrow was Friday.

After Friday it would be Saturday. Davie went sound asleep, right in the middle of a wide smile. In the park across the way, the robins chirped as they settled themselves for the night, and the shamrock grew silently on the windowsill.

The End